ANIMALS

BY DAHLOV IPCAR

FLYING EYE BOOKS

LONDON - NEW YORK

Long, long ago all the animals in the world were wild. Some were timid and hid in the woods, and some were ferocious and dangerous.

Men hunted them for food with spears and bows and arrows. But long ago men learned to tame some of the wild animals.

In the beginning all cats were wild. They hunted in the wild woods for little animals to eat, and they climbed high in the treetops hunting birds.

Now tame cats live with us in our houses and barns and
catch rats and mice.

Once all dogs were wild and fierce. They hunted in packs through the deep, dark forests.

Now men train dogs to guard our houses and to herd sheep and cattle.
And men and dogs go hunting together.

Once all horses were wild. They ran free on the plains in big herds and grazed on the wild grass.

Now most horses live on farms and do farm work, and the farmers take care of them.

People ride horses in rough country where there are no roads, or just for the fun of it.

Once all cattle were wild. They lived in the forests and on the plains.

Now cows are kept on dairy farms to give us milk, and beef cattle are raised on farms and ranches.

Long ago all the pigs lived wild in the woods and ate nuts and roots. They were so fierce that only the bravest men dared to hunt them.

Now most pigs are kept on farms and fed corn and fattened up for market.

Wild sheep and goats lived in the high mountains and jumped from cliff to cliff.

Now tame sheep give us wool, and goats give us milk.

Not only in our own country, but all over the world, these same animals work for man:

cats

dogs

horses

cattle

pigs

sheep

goats

Some of the animals that we see only in the zoo or in the circus work for man, too, in faraway countries

Llamas work in South America carrying burdens up and down steep mountain trails.

In Asia water buffaloes pull plows and do other farm work.

Yaks carry heavy loads in the Himalayan Mountains.

Elephants work in India clearing forests of trees and moving logs and lumber to help build houses.

Camels work in hot, dry desert countries such as Saudi Arabia, because they need very little water to drink.

Reindeer work in Arctic regions such as Lapland, because they can live in the icy, snowy wastes.

Donkeys work in all of these countries and in many other parts of the world.

Ireland

Spain

France

Switzerland

Sicily

Greece

Turkey

Egypt

Africa

India

Mexico

Some animals still live wild in the green jungles of the world.

Some animals still live wild in our own nearby woods.

Sometimes when we walk in the woods we may be
lucky enough to see them.

There are many kinds of animals in the world, wild ones and tame ones.
But the animals that we love the most are our pets that we take care of
and play with and keep just for fun.

Asia

Arctic

Africa

North America

South America

WILD ANIMALS